SUNNY DAY
PUZZLES

over 150 puzzles

Bennie Marcus Collection

About Bonnie Marcus

Bonnie Marcus launched her stylish stationery company, the Bonnie Marcus Collection 'where fashion meets paper®', in 2002 from her dining room table, while expecting her first child. As a former wedding planner in New York City, Marcus was well-known for her event planning expertise and found there was a void in the stationery market in terms of fashion-forward stylish designs. She decided to combine her passion for fashion (having worked for designer Diane von Furstenberg) with her love of event planning and her collection took the stationery industry by storm! Bonnie's stylish designs are now available in thousands of retail stores worldwide and celebrity fans include Cindy Crawford, Christina Aguilera, Britney Spears, Eva Longoria, Marcia Cross and many others. Marcus has been recognized as a pioneer for women in business and is proud to be an established partner of numerous organizations supporting breast cancer awareness. For further information about the company, please visit www.bonniemarcus.com.

This edition published under licence by Exclusive Editions Publishing Ltd in 2015

Exclusive Editions Publishing Ltd
Chartist House
15–17 Trim Street
Bath BA1 1HA, UK
www.parragon.com

Copyright © Parragon Books Ltd 2015
Individual puzzles © Clarity Media
Illustrations supplied courtesy of the © Bonnie Marcus Collection

ISBN 978-1-4723-7592-6

Printed in China

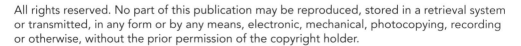

HIDE-AND-SEEK

Can you find the hidden objects in the picture?
Objects may be different in size and colour.

1   2 ✗   3 ♡   4

5 ◁   6   7

ABCDOKU

3			A	1
	E			C
E				
		E5		
D	5	4		

Each square contains a letter and a number. Place 1–5 and A–E once in each row and column to fill the grid. Each combination from A1 through to E5 also appears exactly once in the puzzle.

WORD LADDER

Can you climb the rungs of this word ladder? Change only one letter at each step in order to move from the bottom to the top, and do not rearrange the order of the letters.

DOOR

STEP

WORD PYRAMID

Fill each brick with a single letter to build a pyramid. Each row contains the same bricks as the row beneath but with one missing – however, the order may vary. Each row must spell out a word that matches its clue.

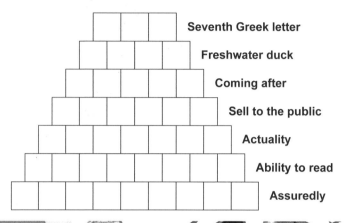

Seventh Greek letter

Freshwater duck

Coming after

Sell to the public

Actuality

Ability to read

Assuredly

SYMBOL VALUES

Each of the four shapes represents a positive whole number. The sum of the shapes in each row and column is displayed at the end of each row and column. Using this information can you work out the numerical value of each shape?

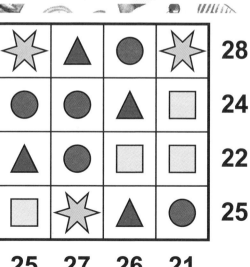

28

24

22

25

25   27   26   21

PATHFINDER

Moving from letter to adjacent letter, can you find a path that visits every square and spells out several **agricultural** words? Start on the shaded square.

I	O	N	F	A	R	R	O	W
T	H	T	E	L	L	I	M	W
A	A	C	K	F	U	R	E	A
N	Y	A	R	E	T	R	E	T
I	S	T	T	I	L	I	N	H
M	G	W	I	L	U	C	G	O
R	E	A	Z	E	R	I	T	R
S	T	R	E	R	F	A	R	M
R	E	H	S	H	T	G	N	I

WORDWHEEL

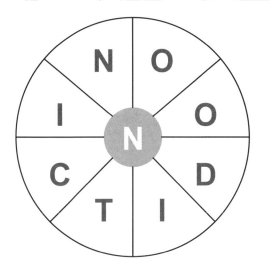

Find as many words of three or more letters in the wheel as you can. Each word must use the central letter and a selection from the outer wheel – no letter may be used more times than it appears in the wheel. Can you find the nine-letter word hidden in the wheel?

KILLER SUDOKU

Place the numbers 1–6 exactly once per row, column, and 3 x 2 bold-lined box.
Additionally the sum total of the squares in each dashed-line shape must match the total given in that shape, and you may not repeat a number within a dashed-line shape.

8	11		4		9
	8		8		
		9	7	9	
9				5	
7			10		8
	14				

SPOT THE DIFFERENCE

Can you spot the eight differences between the two pictures?

BATTLESHIPS

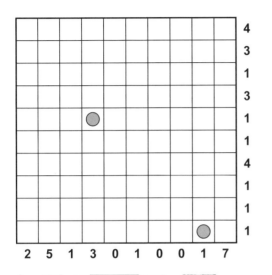

2 5 1 3 0 1 0 0 1 7

Deduce the location of each ship listed below. Numbers around the edge of the grid specify the number of ship segments found in each row and column of the grid. Each ship is surrounded on all sides (horizontally, vertically and diagonally) by water.

SNAKEWORD

There is a nine-letter word hidden in the grid – can you find it? The nine letters form a continuous line passing through each square once, without crossing itself.

R	L	I
E	T	F
A	F	E

9

CROSSWORD

Solve the clues to complete this classic crossword puzzle.

Across

1. Crush with the teeth (6)
5. Dandy (3)
7. Find the solution (5)
8. Lock of curly hair (7)
9. Welsh breed of dog (5)
10. Loss of hearing (8)
12. Supplied or distributed (6)
14. Set of instructions for a dish (6)
17. Creature that eats both meat and plants (8)
18. Reversed (5)
20. More spacious (7)
21. Oneness (5)
22. Make less bright (3)
23. Mineral used to make plaster of Paris (6)

Down

2. Marauders (7)
3. Communities of animals (8)
4. Coalition of countries (4)
5. Italian sports car (7)
6. Stalk joining a leaf to a stem (7)
7. Store in a secret place (5)
11. Laughably small (8)
12. Secured against loss or damage (7)
13. Sports arena (7)
15. Upstart (7)
16. Coarse rock used for polishing (5)
19. Low platform for a lectern (4)

STAR LETTER

Can you find a ten-letter word that can be formed by using the star letter twice, and each other letter once?

CALCUDOKU

Place the numbers from 1–6 once in each row and column, while obeying the sums in the bold-lined regions. The number specifies the total for that region while the operator shows which sum should be applied between the numbers in the region to reach the given total. Numbers may repeat within the bold-lined regions. With subtraction always take the lower numbers away from the highest number in a region, and with division divide the highest number by the lower numbers.

2-		5+	4-	6+	
12+				8x	
6x		17+	4÷		9+
				21+	
8x		11+			
7+					

KAKURO

Fill the white squares so that the total in each across or down run of cells matches the total at the start of that run. You must use the numbers from 1–9 only and cannot repeat a number in a run.

SIMPLE LOOP

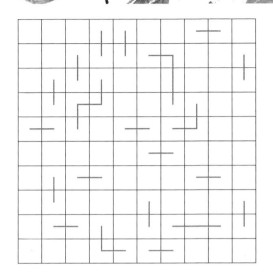

Draw a single, continuous loop that visits every square in the puzzle grid just once. The loop cannot cross itself and must enter and exit each square, so look for instances where there are only two neighbouring squares that can be visited by an empty square.

JIGSAW SUDOKU

Place the numbers 1–9 once in each row, column and bold-lined jigsaw region composed of nine cells.

							5	
			6			9		
6		3	7					
	8			2	1	3		
			1				7	
2			5					

BRIDGES

Connect all the circles (which represent islands) into a single interconnected group.
The number in a circle represents the number of bridges that connect that island to
other islands. Bridges can only be created horizontally or vertically,
with no more than two bridges between any pair of islands. Bridges cannot cross any
other bridges.

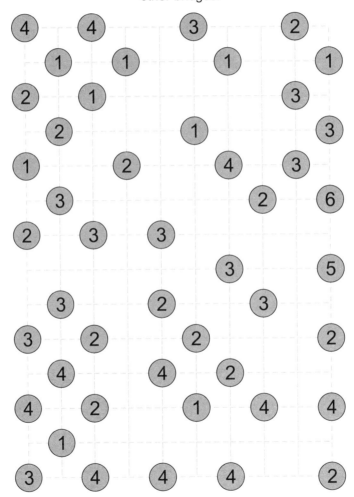

FIND THE SUM

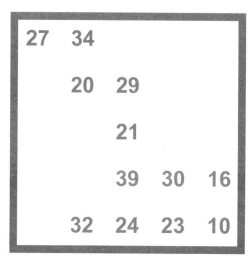

27	34		
	20	29	
	21		
	39	30	16
32	24	23	10

Three of the numbers in this box add up to 102. But can you work out what those three numbers are?

BATTLESHIPS

Deduce the location of each ship listed below. Numbers around the edge of the grid specify the number of ship segments found in each row and column of the grid. Each ship is surrounded on all sides (horizontally, vertically and diagonally) by water.

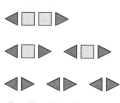

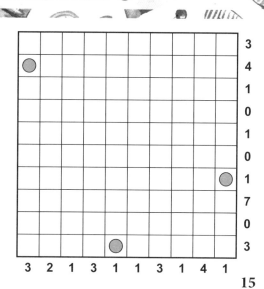

BREEDS OF CAT

Can you find the words in this classic wordsearch grid?

V	A	T	U	E	G	M	E	R	R	A	I	U	I	W
K	T	E	S	R	A	H	A	V	A	N	A	F	B	Q
I	L	A	M	O	S	S	A	N	Y	A	B	M	O	B
S	A	P	E	R	S	I	A	N	X	M	B	F	O	S
U	E	O	Q	K	T	K	A	E	A	R	A	S	S	O
G	G	U	O	G	H	R	S	M	Y	I	L	P	N	P
D	E	R	L	B	T	U	O	T	E	B	I	O	T	E
A	A	R	C	B	I	T	A	S	C	S	N	T	P	R
T	N	T	T	O	N	K	I	N	E	S	E	T	P	O
E	S	A	U	M	J	A	V	A	N	E	S	E	S	P
T	K	T	C	Y	M	R	I	C	W	O	E	D	G	A
U	O	O	C	O	R	N	I	S	H	R	E	X	Q	E
M	S	Z	K	L	R	K	E	I	S	U	A	H	C	V
Q	Y	Z	R	O	O	G	Z	D	A	U	G	Q	A	D
O	L	L	E	H	S	E	S	I	O	T	R	O	T	E

AEGEAN

BALINESE

BIRMAN

BOMBAY

CHAUSIE

CORNISH REX

CYMRIC

HAVANA

JAVANESE

KORAT

MANX

PERSIAN

RUSSIAN BLUE

SIAMESE

SOKOKE

SOMALI

SPOTTED

TONKINESE

TORTOISESHELL

TURKISH

16

FIND THE KEY

Can you find the matching key?

1    2    3

4    5    6

7

BINARY

Fill the grid with 0s and 1s such that 0 and 1 each occur six times in each row and column. The same digit cannot occur in more than two consecutive cells either horizontally or vertically. No whole row can repeat the same series of 0s and 1s as any other row, and no whole column can repeat the same series of 0s and 1s as any other column.

					0		0			1	1
1	1				0					1	
1	0					0					0
			0		1				1		
			0			0		0			
		1							0		
		1			0			1			1
				1		0					
			0								
	1		0								
					1			1	1		
1			1		1					1	

WORD PYRAMID

Fill each brick with a single letter to build a pyramid. Each row contains the same bricks as the row beneath but with one missing – however, the order may vary. Each row must spell out a word that matches its clue.

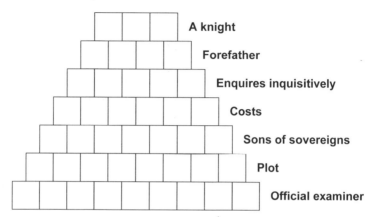

A knight

Forefather

Enquires inquisitively

Costs

Sons of sovereigns

Plot

Official examiner

WORD LADDER

Can you climb the rungs of this word ladder? Change only one letter at each step in order to move from the bottom to the top, and do not rearrange the order of the letters.

GOOD

CALL

19

GOING TRAVELLING

Can you find the words in this classic wordsearch grid?

V	B	V	H	O	T	E	L	L	F	K	Y	E	T	L
E	W	K	D	S	P	C	D	D	I	U	G	E	Q	A
G	T	S	S	J	U	A	C	I	A	M	F	W	M	Y
I	D	S	T	H	G	I	S	S	U	O	M	A	F	E
C	E	K	P	N	E	N	T	S	R	G	R	O	M	A
T	T	P	I	T	A	X	I	C	P	E	O	B	R	I
L	G	A	R	U	N	R	P	P	A	O	W	T	A	B
M	S	C	T	O	E	E	U	L	M	S	R	S	D	P
S	T	K	K	G	D	E	M	A	O	A	E	T	V	V
I	U	I	R	N	X	A	R	E	T	R	C	O	E	K
R	L	N	O	I	T	A	N	I	T	S	E	D	N	O
U	E	G	W	T	A	K	P	T	L	I	E	S	T	U
O	R	T	K	A	E	R	B	Y	T	I	C	R	U	P
T	I	C	K	E	T	S	L	Y	P	A	S	X	R	D
C	U	L	T	U	R	E	N	A	L	P	O	R	E	A

ABROAD

ADVENTURE

AEROPLANE

CAMPING

CITY BREAK

CULTURE

DESTINATION

EATING OUT

EXCITEMENT

EXPLORE

FAMOUS SIGHTS

GUIDE

HOTEL

PACKING

PASSPORT

RESTAURANTS

SUITCASE

TICKETS

TOURISM

WORK TRIP

LETTERFIT

Can you place each of these words once in the grid to create a filled crossword grid?

4 letters

Awry
Ekes
Item
Uses

5 letters

Ovals
Rules

6 letters

Adorer
Innate
Pellet
Tedium
Thrill
Tussle

7 letters

Airline
Insular
Lacquer
Optical
Resided
Rounded

8 letters

Apposite
Brimless
Moderate
Override

9 letters

Courtroom
Suspected

WORDWHEEL

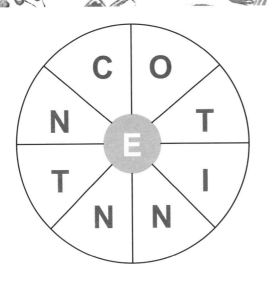

Find as many words of three or more letters in the wheel as you can. Each word must use the central letter and a selection from the outer wheel – no letter may be used more times than it appears in the wheel. Can you find the nine-letter word hidden in the wheel?

BATTLESHIPS

Deduce the location of each ship listed below. Numbers around the edge of the grid specify the number of ship segments found in each row and column of the grid. Each ship is surrounded on all sides (horizontally, vertically and diagonally) by water.

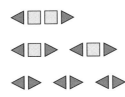

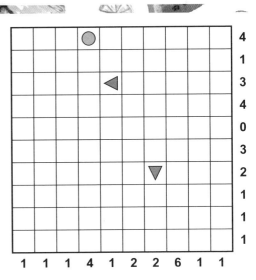

BRIDGES

Connect all the circles (which represent islands) into a single interconnected group.
The number in a circle represents the number of bridges that connect that island to
other islands. Bridges can only be created horizontally or vertically,
with no more than two bridges between any pair of islands. Bridges cannot cross any
other bridges.

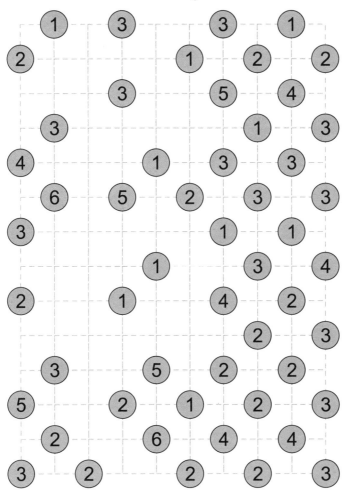

SNAKEWORD

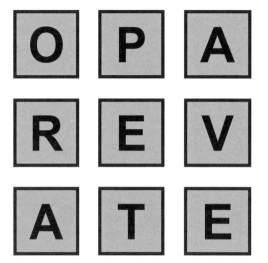

There is a nine-letter word hidden in the grid – can you find it? The nine letters form a continuous line passing through each square once, without crossing itself.

STAR LETTER

Can you find a ten-letter word that can be formed by using the star letter twice, and each other letter once?

PATHFINDER

Moving from letter to adjacent letter, can you find a path that visits every square and spells out the names of several **constellations**? Start on the shaded square.

N	Y	U	S	A	G	E	P	S
X	L	S	R	U	S	S	M	N
C	N	A	D	A	N	I	A	E
E	I	H	Y	C	G	A	J	P
T	R	A	L	A	R	T	O	R
U	S	C	I	S	U	R	R	E
N	A	Q	U	H	E	E	L	S
O	O	M	E	A	R	C	A	S
I	R	U	L	C	C	U	L	E

LETTERFIT

Can you place each of these words once in the grid to create a filled crossword grid?

4 letters

Lark
Uses

5 letters

Ceded
Easel
Empty
Exact
Fjord
Issue
Sense
Sweat
Wrote
Yarns

6 letters

Breeze
Neural
Shower
Squads

7 letters

Assures
Asunder
Buzzers
Implode
Inkwell
Sheeted
Sojourn
Wizened

9 letters

Advertise

SYMBOL VALUES

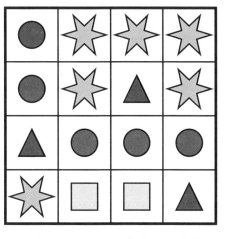

15

16

22

17

19 17 18 16

Each of the four shapes represents a positive whole number. The sum of the shapes in each row and column is displayed at the end of each row and column. Using this information can you work out the numerical value of each shape?

ABC LOGIC

Place the letters A, B and C exactly once in each row and column. Each row and column has two blank cells. The letters at the edge of a row/column indicate which of the letters is the first/last to appear in that row/column.

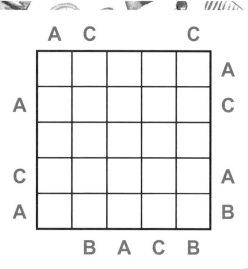

27

BRIDGES

Connect all the circles (which represent islands) into a single interconnected group. The number in a circle represents the number of bridges that connect that island to other islands. Bridges can only be created horizontally or vertically, with no more than two bridges between any pair of islands. Bridges cannot cross any other bridges.

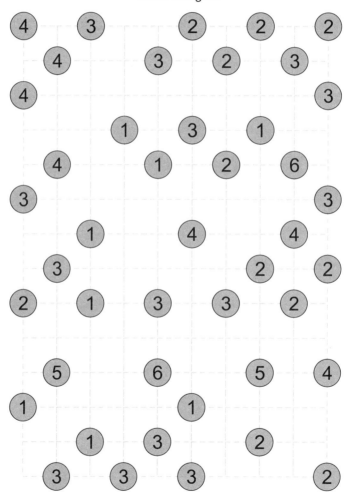

MEMORY PUZZLE

Study the picture carefully for 30 seconds. Without looking back, can you write the number of each of these listed elements of the picture in the correct square of the grid?

1 Birds
2 Coconuts
3 Ball
4 Starfish
5 Surfer
6 Sun
7 Bucket
8 Kite

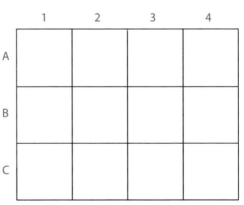

ABCDoku

A	5			
	A	C4		2
	4	D	B	3
B				

Each square contains a letter and a number. Place 1–5 and A–E once in each row and column to fill the grid. Each combination from A1 through to E5 also appears exactly once in the puzzle.

SNAKEWORD

There is a nine-letter word hidden in the grid – can you find it? The nine letters form a continuous line passing through each square once, without crossing itself.

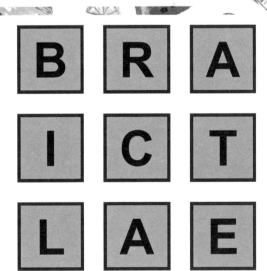

BATTLESHIPS

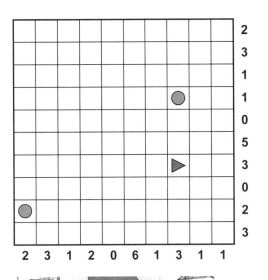

Row clues (top to bottom): 2, 3, 1, 1, 0, 5, 3, 0, 2, 3

Column clues (left to right): 2, 3, 1, 2, 0, 6, 1, 3, 1, 1

Deduce the location of each ship listed below. Numbers around the edge of the grid specify the number of ship segments found in each row and column of the grid. Each ship is surrounded on all sides (horizontally, vertically and diagonally) by water.

JIGSAW SUDOKU

Place the numbers 1–9 once in each row, column and bold-lined jigsaw region composed of nine cells.

				8	7			
					9			3
	4		1			9		
			2				1	
3	5							8
6							4	
						5		

31

PATHFINDER

Moving from letter to adjacent letter, can you find a path that visits every square and spells out several words relating to **the pub**? Start on the shaded square.

A	P	P	R	L	E	R	C	R
H	L	Y	U	A	G	P	S	I
R	E	H	O	C	S	S	B	E
R	A	T	A	R	R	B	T	V
S	B	C	S	N	E	E	H	E
R	A	H	G	E	L	O	G	R
U	L	I	N	W	D	R	U	A
G	R	E	P	S	N	D	A	G
E	R	P	A	L	A	D	R	E

CALCUDOKU

7+		2-	1-		9+
8+			16+	4-	
10+					
		12+		11+	
6+				9+	
	11+		2÷		

Place the numbers from 1–6 once in each row and column, while obeying the sums in the bold-lined regions. The number specifies the total for that region while the operator shows which sum should be applied between the numbers in the region to reach the given total. Numbers may repeat within the bold-lined regions. With subtraction always take the lower numbers away from the highest number in a region, and with division divide the highest number by the lower numbers.

BATTLESHIPS

Deduce the location of each ship listed below. Numbers around the edge of the grid specify the number of ship segments found in each row and column of the grid. Each ship is surrounded on all sides (horizontally, vertically and diagonally) by water.

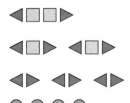

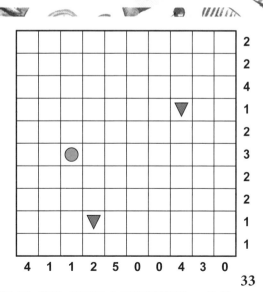

BRIDGES

Connect all the circles (which represent islands) into a single interconnected group.
The number in a circle represents the number of bridges that connect that island to
other islands. Bridges can only be created horizontally or vertically,
with no more than two bridges between any pair of islands. Bridges cannot cross any
other bridges.

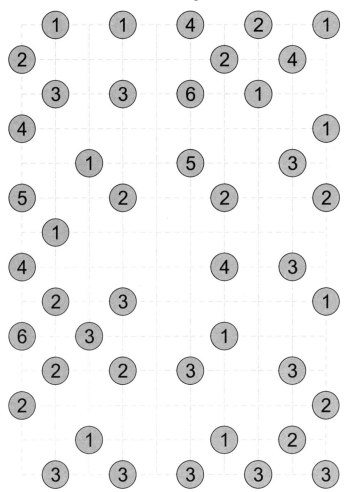

KAKURO

Fill the white squares so that the total in each across or down run of cells matches the total at the start of that run. You must use the numbers from 1–9 only and cannot repeat a number in a run.

SIMPLE LOOP

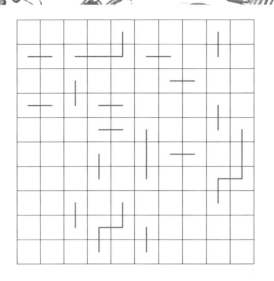

Draw a single, continuous loop that visits every square in the puzzle grid just once. The loop cannot cross itself and must enter and exit each square, so look for instances where there are only two neighbouring squares that can be visited by an empty square.

FIND THE SUM

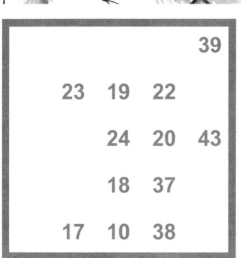

			39
23	19	22	
	24	20	43
	18	37	
17	10	38	

Three of the numbers in this box add up to 118. But can you work out what those three numbers are?

CROSSWORD

Solve the clues to complete this classic crossword puzzle.

Across

1 Female officer of the law (11)
9 Eats like a bird (5)
10 Come together (3)
11 Declare invalid (5)
12 Unit of heat (5)
13 Bulbous plant (8)
16 City in NE Scotland (8)
18 Spanish wine (5)
21 Religious table (5)
22 Organ of sight (3)
23 Epic poem ascribed to Homer (5)
24 Amazing (11)

Down

2 Belief (7)
3 Collapse violently inwards (7)
4 Old Portuguese currency (6)
5 Beginning of something (5)
6 Debate in a heated manner (5)
7 Moved goods (11)
8 Poorly behaved; impolite (3-8)
14 Width (7)
15 Subdivision (7)
17 Swimming costume (6)
19 Removes the lid (5)
20 Friend (Spanish) (5)

LETTERFIT

Can you place each of these words once in the grid to create a filled crossword grid?

4 letters

Asks
Race

5 letters

Camel
Comic
Inept
Mince
Nears
Pilot

6 letters

Onward
Scampi
Sneers
Symbol

7 letters

Anarchy
Bandage
Commute
Rooftop
Symptom
Weakest

8 letters

Assessor
Nutshell

12 letters

Butterscotch
Encroachment

13 letters

Receptiveness
Reciprocation

Killer Sudoku

Place the numbers 1–6 exactly once per row, column and 3 x 2 bold-lined box.
Additionally the sum total of the squares in each dashed-line shape must match the total given in that shape, and you may not repeat a number within a dashed-line shape.

4		12			12
13			5		
9	7			9	8
	9	5			
		8	11		7
7					

Find the Phrase

Can you find the phrase represented by the image to the right?

CHEMICAL ELEMENTS

Can you find the words in this classic wordsearch grid?

```
S  S  D  U  T  R  K  A  L  S  T  O  B  X  A
K  O  U  M  M  P  Q  R  W  P  R  W  E  D  V
R  S  T  U  N  J  L  U  Q  U  A  N  P  E  E
E  N  I  M  O  R  B  I  F  T  O  R  X  I  A
V  H  L  Q  T  G  O  L  D  N  W  U  G  T  R
L  R  Y  K  P  B  U  T  C  O  C  O  T  O  H
I  O  P  D  Y  O  G  H  A  C  A  R  B  O  N
S  X  A  U  R  R  L  M  L  I  T  H  I  U  M
G  Y  B  I  K  O  L  S  U  L  M  S  S  S  B
I  G  N  R  R  N  G  Q  M  I  U  N  A  T  R
A  E  Y  I  U  B  U  E  I  S  L  S  U  F  W
L  N  P  L  A  T  I  N  U  M  E  E  L  C
N  E  N  E  G  O  R  T  I  N  W  K  H  P  S
P  B  E  R  Y  L  L  I  U  M  P  R  E  S  T
P  O  T  A  S  S  I  U  M  R  V  L  S  E  F
```

ALUMINIUM	HYDROGEN
ARGON	KRYPTON
BERYLLIUM	LITHIUM
BORON	NITROGEN
BROMINE	OXYGEN
CARBON	PLATINUM
CHLORINE	POTASSIUM
FLUORINE	SILICON
GOLD	SILVER
HELIUM	XENON

WORD LADDER

LAST

TIME

Can you climb the rungs of this word ladder? Change only one letter at each step in order to move from the bottom to the top, and do not rearrange the order of the letters.

JIGSAW SUDOKU

Place the numbers 1–9 once in each row, column and bold-lined jigsaw region composed of nine cells.

		5				1		6
			2	7		5		
1		6			9			8
5		7						3
		3			8			
		4	1					
						3		
							9	
					7			5

SNAKEWORD

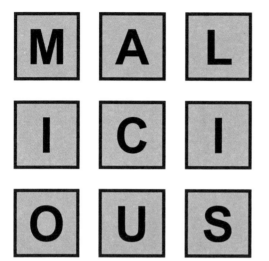

There is a nine-letter word hidden in the grid – can you find it? The nine letters form a continuous line passing through each square once, without crossing itself.

ABC LOGIC

Place the letters A, B and C exactly once in each row and column. Each row and column has two blank cells. The letters at the edge of a row/column indicate which of the letters is the first/last to appear in that row/column.

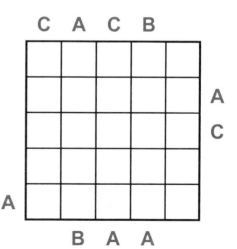

CROSSWORD

Solve the clues to complete this classic crossword puzzle.

Across

1 Science of communications (11)
9 Number in a trio (5)
10 Circulating life force (3)
11 Pertaining to the sun (5)
12 Pay out money (5)
13 Cloudy and dull (8)
16 Absolute (8)
18 Monotonous hum (5)
21 Value (5)
22 Strange (3)
23 Undo (5)
24 One who held a job previously (11)

Down

2 Surrendered (7)
3 Remove (7)
4 Hospital carers (6)
5 Arduous journeys (5)
6 A hidden storage space (5)
7 Action of ending a partnership (11)
8 Ornithologist (11)
14 Eg daffodils (7)
15 Sign of the zodiac (7)
17 Adhesive putty (6)
19 Detection technology (5)
20 Shape (5)

BINARY

Fill the grid with 0s and 1s such that 0 and 1 each occur six times in each row and column. The same digit cannot occur in more than two consecutive cells either horizontally or vertically. No whole row can repeat the same series of 0s and 1s as any other row, and no whole column can repeat the same series of 0s and 1s as any other column.

				1		0			1		
			1		1	0		0			
		0									
	1	1			0						1
	0					1					
1									1		
1	1		1			0	0				
			0	1					0		
	1							1			1
										0	
1		0	1								

ABCDOKU

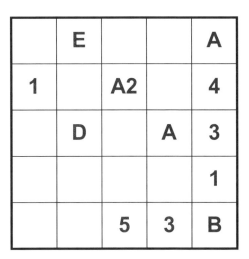

Each square contains a letter and a number. Place 1–5 and A–E once in each row and column to fill the grid. Each combination from A1 through to E5 also appears exactly once in the puzzle.

	E			A
1		A2		4
	D		A	3
				1
		5	3	B

STAR LETTER

Can you find a ten-letter word that can be formed by using the star letter twice, and each other letter once?

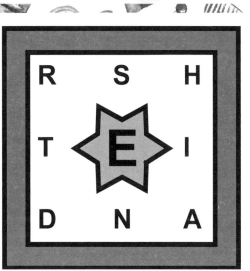

R S H

T **E** I

D N A

CALCUDOKU

3-	3-	12+			2÷
		6÷			
3-	12x	8+		12x	
		2÷	13+	1-	
5÷				7+	
12+				2-	

Place the numbers from 1–6 once in each row and column, while obeying the sums in the bold-lined regions. The number specifies the total for that region while the operator shows which sum should be applied between the numbers in the region to reach the given total. Numbers may repeat within the bold-lined regions. With subtraction always take the lower numbers away from the highest number in a region, and with division divide the highest number by the lower numbers.

ABC LOGIC

Place the letters A, B and C exactly once in each row and column. Each row and column has two blank cells. The letters at the edge of a row/column indicate which of the letters is the first/last to appear in that row/column.

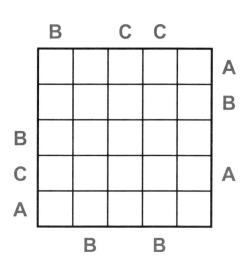

HALLOWEEN

Can you find the words in this classic wordsearch grid?

```
T T R I C K O R T R E A T S A
R L A N T E R N O R D L U A C
A A O L T A T C R E E P Y Q X
R E I P I S A B O N E S V O Q
D H N U O X F Z P R U A E O D
U A I M X R T L S Y M G G L C
U U L P N P B T O P K E R L I
T N B K S N I F I W M O O R B
S T O I L T D R O M E J O Y V
H E G N I N E T H G I R F P P
F D H O L P U N O T E L E K S
F A N C Y D R E S S M C H W C
A C O S T U M E M O S Q R O A
A U D U V I I X I H I Z P M R
W R M H G A W S R G T S P R Y
```

BONES	LANTERN
BROOM	PUMPKIN
CAULDRON	SCARY
COSTUME	SKELETON
CREEPY	SPOOKY
FANCY DRESS	SUPERSTITION
FRIGHTENING	TRICK OR TREAT
GHOST	VAMPIRE
GOBLIN	WEREWOLF
HAUNTED	WITCHES

BINARY

Fill the grid with 0s and 1s such that 0 and 1 each occur six times in each row and column. The same digit cannot occur in more than two consecutive cells either horizontally or vertically. No whole row can repeat the same series of 0s and 1s as any other row, and no whole column can repeat the same series of 0s and 1s as any other column.

1				1		0					
		1	1			1			0	0	
						1					
	0	0				0					
1						1				0	
			1								
			1		1		1		1		
								0			
1											
0	1	0						1	1		
	1	1	0					1			
		0	1								

WORD PYRAMID

Fill each brick with a single letter to build a pyramid. Each row contains the same bricks as the row beneath but with one missing – however, the order may vary. Each row must spell out a word that matches its clue.

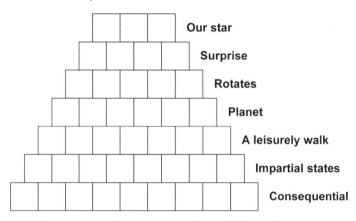

- Our star
- Surprise
- Rotates
- Planet
- A leisurely walk
- Impartial states
- Consequential

BATTLESHIPS

Deduce the location of each ship listed below. Numbers around the edge of the grid specify the number of ship segments found in each row and column of the grid. Each ship is surrounded on all sides (horizontally, vertically and diagonally) by water.

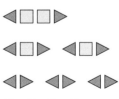

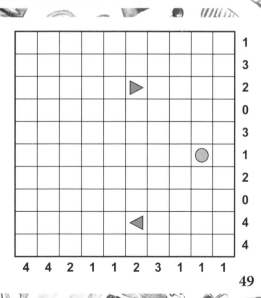

SYMBOL VALUES

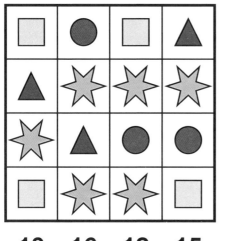

14
15
17
10

13 16 12 15

Each of the four shapes represents a positive whole number. The sum of the shapes in each row and column is displayed at the end of each row and column. Using this information can you work out the numerical value of each shape?

CALCUDOKU

Place the numbers from 1–6 once in each row and column, while obeying the sums in the bold-lined regions. The number specifies the total for that region while the operator shows which sum should be applied between the numbers in the region to reach the given total. Numbers may repeat within the bold-lined regions. With subtraction always take the lower numbers away from the highest number in a region, and with division divide the highest number by the lower numbers.

10+	6÷		16+		
		5-			6+
8+		20x			
3-		12+	9+		12+
3x			15+		
	6+				

50

CROSSWORD

Solve the clues to complete this classic crossword puzzle.

Across

1 Slender freshwater fish (4)
3 Car light (8)
9 Small onion-like bulb (7)
10 Managed (5)
11 Cooling device in the kitchen (12)
13 Divide into two parts (6)
15 Small summer-house (6)
17 Dark towering cloud (12)
20 One of the United Arab Emirates (5)
21 Closing sections of compositions (7)
22 Abruptly (8)
23 Potential applications (4)

Down

1 Explain using words (8)
2 Finely cut straw (5)
4 Dish served at a formal dinner (6)
5 Formal announcements (12)
6 Sanction (7)
7 Seed containers (4)
8 Type of holiday package (3-9)
12 Is composed of (8)
14 ___ out: extinguished a cigarette (7)
16 Wretched (6)
18 Charges (a sum of money) (5)
19 Appends (4)

Killer Sudoku

7		10	10		
9	3		10		9
				11	
11	12				11
		8			
8		7			

Place the numbers 1–6 exactly once per row, column and 3 x 2 bold-lined box. Additionally the sum total of the squares in each dashed-line shape must match the total given in that shape, and you may not repeat a number within a dashed-line shape.

Snakeword

There is a nine-letter word hidden in the grid – can you find it? The nine letters form a continuous line passing through each square once, without crossing itself.

C	A	G
H	P	N
A	M	E

PATHFINDER

Moving from letter to adjacent letter, can you find a path that visits every square and spells out several words relating to **bonfire night**? Start on the shaded square.

K	E	S	D	I	S	A	Y	B
W	O	I	R	B	P	L	N	A
A	N	T	A	E	L	K	G	S
F	R	C	E	L	E	R	A	P
Y	O	L	E	S	R	L	E	O
U	M	A	E	H	W	Z	Z	U
G	E	N	C	A	E	N	I	T
A	D	C	E	N	R	I	F	C
C	S	A	L	D	E	H	T	A

SIMPLE LOOP

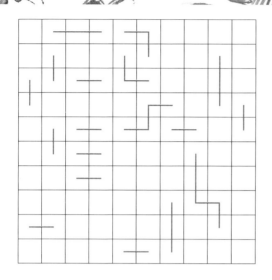

Draw a single, continuous loop that visits every square in the puzzle grid just once. The loop cannot cross itself and must enter and exit each square, so look for instances where there are only two neighbouring squares that can be visited by an empty square.

FIND THE PHRASE

Can you find the phrase represented by the image to the right?

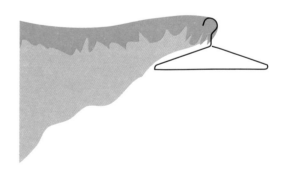

KAKURO

Fill the white squares so that the total in each across or down run of cells matches the total at the start of that run. You must use the numbers from 1–9 only and cannot repeat a number in a run.

COLOURS

Can you find the words in this classic wordsearch grid?

```
I  A  Q  T  S  Y  H  T  E  M  A  C  R  A  N
U  T  E  L  I  O  D  W  W  P  J  O  L  V  S
L  F  A  U  B  U  R  N  R  K  T  B  G  C  P
A  I  S  H  C  U  F  S  U  C  E  A  C  N  J
V  Y  R  L  A  Q  I  P  C  G  L  L  M  T  A
E  J  T  E  N  I  R  A  M  A  R  T  L  U  P
N  E  T  A  L  O  C  O  H  C  A  U  A  N  T
D  A  O  A  E  K  Q  U  R  T  C  R  B  T  I
E  N  I  R  E  G  N  A  T  T  S  Q  L  S  F
R  M  D  D  A  Q  I  I  F  O  E  U  A  E  X
Y  O  E  F  I  N  W  E  W  C  S  O  C  H  T
M  Z  A  R  A  R  G  F  B  I  I  K  C  O
T  Y  I  O  A  N  I  E  E  R  R  S  S  N  O
N  E  U  T  O  L  S  V  T  P  E  E  U  F  D
T  M  X  O  C  A  D  Q  T  A  C  M  P  Y  C
```

AMETHYST	EMERALD
APRICOT	FUCHSIA
AUBURN	LAVENDER
BEIGE	ORANGE
BLACK	PERIWINKLE
BURGUNDY	SCARLET
CERISE	TANGERINE
CHESTNUT	TURQUOISE
CHOCOLATE	ULTRAMARINE
COBALT	VIRIDIAN

WORD LADDER

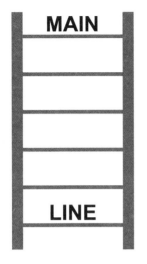

MAIN

LINE

Can you climb the rungs of this word ladder? Change only one letter at each step in order to move from the bottom to the top, and do not rearrange the order of the letters.

SYMBOL VALUES

Each of the four shapes represents a positive whole number. The sum of the shapes in each row and column is displayed at the end of each row and column. Using this information can you work out the numerical value of each shape?

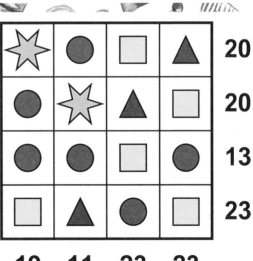

★	●	☐	▲	**20**
●	★	▲	☐	**20**
●	●	☐	●	**13**
☐	▲	●	☐	**23**
19	**11**	**23**	**23**	

CROSSWORD

Solve the clues to complete this classic crossword puzzle.

Across

7 Expels air abruptly (6)
8 Expensive white fur (6)
10 Qualification attached to a statement (7)
11 Metric unit of capacity (5)
12 Long grass (4)
13 Large African antelope (5)
17 ___ Avenue: NY shopping thoroughfare (5)
18 Capital of Norway (4)
22 Assumed proposition (5)
23 Spouts (7)
24 Scottish sheep dog (6)
25 Agreement or concord (6)

Down

1 Type of staff (7)
2 Taught (7)
3 Seat (5)
4 Increase the duration of (7)
5 Goes through in detail; filters (5)
6 Discourage (5)
9 Contaminant (9)
14 Of great size (7)
15 Serving no purpose (7)
16 Accommodation (7)
19 Choose to do something (5)
20 Stroll casually (5)
21 Form of oxygen (5)

FIND THE SUM

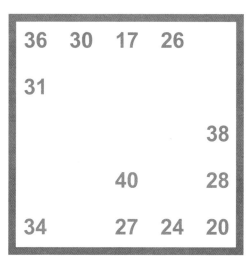

36	30	17	26
31			
			38
		40	28
34		27	24	20

Three of the numbers in this box add up to 65. But can you work out what those three numbers are?

ABC LOGIC

Place the letters A, B and C exactly once in each row and column. Each row and column has two blank cells. The letters at the edge of a row/column indicate which of the letters is the first/last to appear in that row/column.

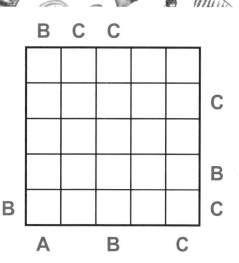

BRIDGES

Connect all the circles (which represent islands) into a single interconnected group. The number in a circle represents the number of bridges that connect that island to other islands. Bridges can only be created horizontally or vertically, with no more than two bridges between any pair of islands. Bridges cannot cross any other bridges.

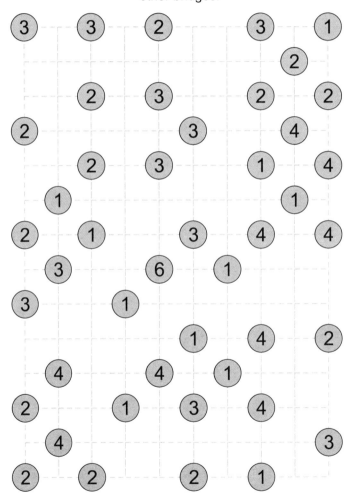

PATHFINDER

Moving from letter to adjacent letter, can you find a path that visits every square and spells out several words relating to **cricket**? Start on the shaded square.

B	E	E	R	F	O	U	A	I
O	S	A	C	R	E	R	M	D
U	E	E	P	P	P	R	E	E
N	W	S	E	I	O	B	G	N
D	R	O	S	L	W	L	N	F
A	L	U	R	F	R	E	I	I
R	L	N	E	V	E	R	W	E
Y	A	D	E	R	I	N	S	L
E	R	I	P	M	U	R	E	D

STAR LETTER

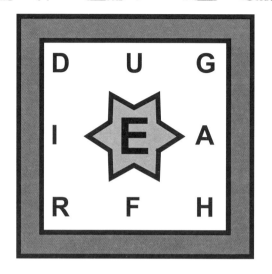

Can you find a ten-letter word that can be formed by using the star letter twice, and each other letter once?

JIGSAW SUDOKU

Place the numbers 1–9 once in each row, column and bold-lined jigsaw region composed of nine cells.

				4				9
	8				5			
		2				1		8
								1
6	5		3	2				
9					4			
	7	5			3	8		
	4			1				

HEALTHY EATING

Can you find the words in this classic wordsearch grid?

```
R  B  L  Z  M  V  V  P  K  B  A  N  N  E  Y
G  P  A  W  N  O  I  N  O  M  E  L  O  N  U
W  O  Y  N  V  B  O  S  T  A  M  S  E  P  E
R  M  R  B  A  W  Y  R  R  E  H  C  U  R  Z
S  E  T  U  R  N  I  P  H  W  M  V  I  P  G
U  G  C  L  W  O  A  S  O  S  S  A  U  I  R
Y  R  R  E  B  W  A  R  T  S  U  T  A  F  L
Y  A  A  A  L  S  T  D  F  B  G  M  U  G  F
G  N  S  A  P  E  G  A  B  B  A  C  A  E  F
V  A  P  U  V  E  R  F  E  E  R  A  T  D  T
L  T  B  A  Z  O  F  Y  I  M  A  I  Y  O  Z
I  E  E  A  I  A  C  R  F  G  P  N  Q  B  T
T  M  R  E  L  P  P  A  U  G  S  Q  P  O  T
X  H  R  N  O  S  M  A  D  I  A  H  E  J  I
I  A  Y  I  A  P  R  I  C  O  T  G  G  S  F
```

APPLE	FIGS
APRICOT	GRAPEFRUIT
ASPARAGUS	LEMON
AVOCADO	MELON
BANANA	MUSHROOM
BROAD BEAN	ONION
CABBAGE	POMEGRANATE
CELERY	RASPBERRY
CHERRY	STRAWBERRY
DAMSON	TURNIP

63

SIMPLE LOOP

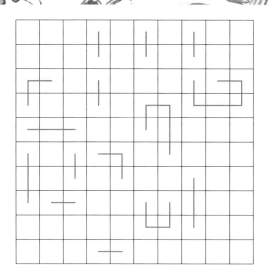

Draw a single, continuous loop that visits every square in the puzzle grid just once. The loop cannot cross itself and must enter and exit each square, so look for instances where there are only two neighbouring squares that can be visited by an empty square.

KILLER SUDOKU

Place the numbers 1–6 exactly once per row, column and 3 x 2 bold-lined box. Additionally the sum total of the squares in each dashed-line shape must match the total given in that shape, and you may not repeat a number within a dashed-line shape.

8		14	8		
5				7	
4		11		15	7
8	11	5			
			7		
7				9	

CALCUDOKU

11+	1-		10+	15x	
	3-	3-		5+	
			6+	12+	30x
10+					
15+	10+				4÷
		5÷			

Place the numbers from 1–6 once in each row and column, while obeying the sums in the bold-lined regions. The number specifies the total for that region while the operator shows which sum should be applied between the numbers in the region to reach the given total. Numbers may repeat within the bold-lined regions. With subtraction always take the lower numbers away from the highest number in a region, and with division divide the highest number by the lower numbers.

BATTLESHIPS

Deduce the location of each ship listed below. Numbers around the edge of the grid specify the number of ship segments found in each row and column of the grid. Each ship is surrounded on all sides (horizontally, vertically and diagonally) by water.

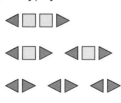

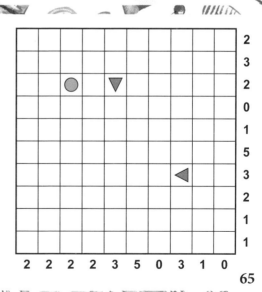

SYMBOL VALUES

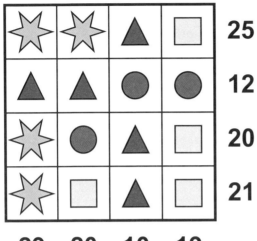

Each of the four shapes represents a positive whole number. The sum of the shapes in each row and column is displayed at the end of each row and column. Using this information can you work out the numerical value of each shape?

ABC LOGIC

Place the letters A, B and C exactly once in each row and column. Each row and column has two blank cells. The letters at the edge of a row/column indicate which of the letters is the first/last to appear in that row/column.

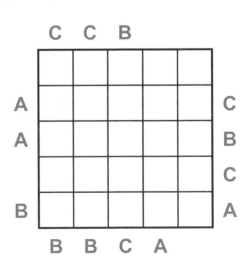

LETTERFIT

Can you place each of these words once in the grid to create a filled crossword grid?

3 letters

Lad
Odd

4 letters

Acne
Coup
Drab
Dune
Ruff
Urge

5 letters

Acids
Edits
Flora
Heist
Meals
Rebut
Sever
Under

6 letters

Dreads
Exhale
Miscue
Sordid

7 letters

Imitate
Studied

8 letters

Educator
Pleasant
Putative
Reawaken

9 letters

Chihuahua
Inductive

67

BRIDGES

Connect all the circles (which represent islands) into a single interconnected group. The number in a circle represents the number of bridges that connect that island to other islands. Bridges can only be created horizontally or vertically, with no more than two bridges between any pair of islands. Bridges cannot cross any other bridges.

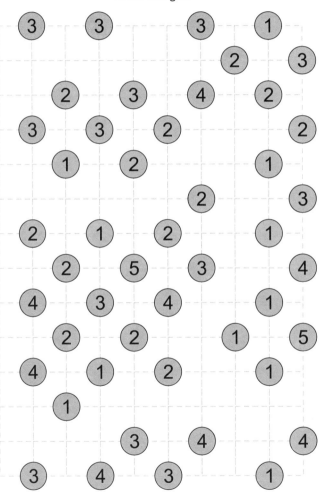

PATHFINDER

Moving from letter to adjacent letter, can you find a path that visits every square and spells out several **boys' names**? Start on the shaded square.

H	A	M	C	H	R	E	D	E
A	G	R	E	A	F	S	W	D
R	E	O	D	R	L	E	A	R
G	D	R	N	A	L	I	B	D
A	R	G	E	X	L	Y	T	P
H	C	I	G	E	L	A	R	E
T	H	R	R	O	R	Y	A	T
T	E	W	E	G	N	A	U	E
A	M	W	E	R	D	S	T	R

WORDWHEEL

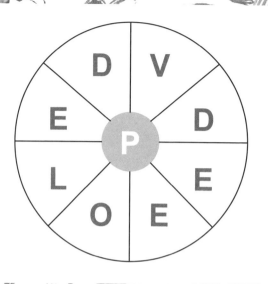

Find as many words of three or more letters in the wheel as you can. Each word must use the central letter and a selection from the outer wheel – no letter may be used more times than it appears in the wheel. Can you find the nine-letter word hidden in the wheel?

STAR LETTER

Can you find a ten-letter word that can be formed by using the star letter twice, and each other letter once?

COUNTRIES

Can you find the words in this classic wordsearch grid?

```
E S N I S Y U T D T O L K Y Z
G G V D A R V K D C O U K G L
M E X I C O V B P O A S R R I
H R R T U S Y O G W U P A E V
H M T U J Y R L E T S P M E I
A A A T S T D I A A T S N C I
P N I L U S N V W T R S E E A
S Y N G L G I I B Q I L D I I
I I A U S T R A L I A I N R N
W L U U Y A W R O N S A A Q O
A V H R G A B R D O B I L W T
Y X T F H A O Q H L S D N G S
S W I T Z E R L A N D N I N E
T O L B U L G A R I A I F A R
P L F X M L L L P R M T K O Y
```

ALBANIA	ICELAND
AUSTRALIA	INDIA
AUSTRIA	ITALY
BOLIVIA	LITHUANIA
BULGARIA	MEXICO
DENMARK	NORWAY
ESTONIA	PARAGUAY
FINLAND	PORTUGAL
GERMANY	RUSSIA
GREECE	SWITZERLAND

BINARY

Fill the grid with 0s and 1s such that 0 and 1 each occur six times in each row and column. The same digit cannot occur in more than two consecutive cells either horizontally or vertically. No whole row can repeat the same series of 0s and 1s as any other row, and no whole column can repeat the same series of 0s and 1s as any column.

							1				
	0	0				1	0				
		0							1		
			1	1						0	
0			1			1	0				
0			1			1			0		0
		0							0		
			1		1						
						0			0		0
			0			0					0
	0		0	0							
						1				0	0

CROSSWORD

Solve the clues to complete this classic crossword puzzle.

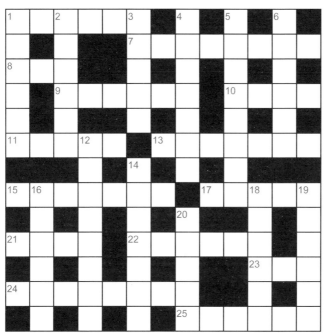

Across

1 Erase a mark from a surface (6)
7 Predicament (8)
8 Flat-topped cap with a tassel (3)
9 Group of 12 constellations (6)
10 Cooking appliance (4)
11 Sediment (5)
13 Clergymen (7)
15 Bad-tempered (7)
17 Refute by evidence (5)
21 Insect larva (4)
22 Had a very strong smell (6)
23 Unwell (3)
24 Confined as a prisoner (8)
25 Oxford ___ : famous London
   road (6)

Down

1 Envelop (6)
2 End disappointingly (6)
3 Supply with; furnish (5)
4 Draw level (5,2)
5 Publicly recommend (8)
6 Current of air (6)
12 Complains (8)
14 Garnish (anag) (7)
16 Very enthusiastic and eager (6)
18 Part of a dress (6)
19 Plaque (6)
20 Gives a meal to (5)

BATTLESHIPS

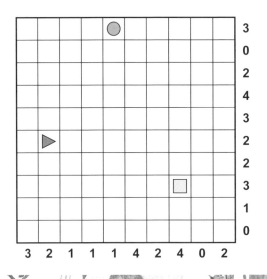

| 3 |
| 0 |
| 2 |
| 4 |
| 3 |
| 2 |
| 2 |
| 3 |
| 1 |
| 0 |

3 2 1 1 1 4 2 4 0 2

Deduce the location of each ship listed below. Numbers around the edge of the grid specify the number of ship segments found in each row and column of the grid. Each ship is surrounded on all sides (horizontally, vertically and diagonally) by water.

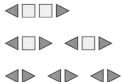

SNAKEWORD

There is a nine-letter word hidden in the grid – can you find it? The nine letters form a continuous line passing through each square once, without crossing itself.

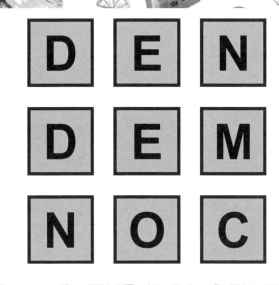

D	E	N
D	E	M
N	O	C

KAKURO

Fill the white squares so that the total in each across or down run of cells matches the total at the start of that run. You must use the numbers from 1–9 only and cannot repeat a number in a run.

JIGSAW SUDOKU

Place the numbers 1–9 once in each row, column and bold-lined jigsaw region composed of nine cells.

SNAKEWORD

There is a nine-letter word hidden in the grid – can you find it? The nine letters form a continuous line passing through each square once, without crossing itself.

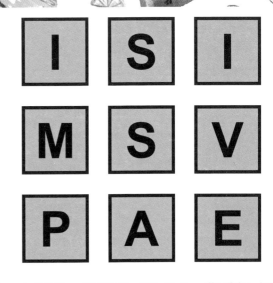

JOB TITLES

Can you find the words in this classic wordsearch grid?

```
H  T  S  T  P  T  A  Y  L  K  L  A  X  D  O
R  E  P  O  R  T  E  R  E  M  R  A  F  M  I
K  A  H  B  T  C  E  T  I  H  C  R  A  S  T
S  C  O  R  E  T  H  G  I  F  E  R  I  F  P
G  H  T  N  O  N  N  V  D  N  L  A  U  O  G
A  E  O  A  M  Y  A  A  G  U  W  X  L  Y  A
V  R  G  I  R  U  E  I  T  T  J  I  T  R  U
F  E  R  R  V  J  S  V  C  N  T  I  E  A  F
T  T  A  A  Y  E  R  I  R  I  U  R  W  T  W
O  I  P  R  D  A  U  S  C  U  N  O  U  E  Q
P  R  H  B  L  C  N  I  M  I  S  H  C  R  Z
E  W  E  I  Y  R  A  U  T  C  A  M  C  C  N
E  W  R  L  A  N  A  L  Y  S  T  N  H  E  A
Y  T  Y  M  I  B  D  Y  D  A  R  T  I  S  T
R  O  V  C  S  K  X  P  R  Q  E  O  N  R  E
```

ACCOUNTANT	NURSE
ACTUARY	PHOTOGRAPHER
ANALYST	POLITICIAN
ARCHITECT	REPORTER
ARTIST	SECRETARY
FARMER	SURVEYOR
FIREFIGHTER	TEACHER
JUDGE	TECHNICIAN
LIBRARIAN	WEB DESIGNER
MUSICIAN	WRITER

SNAKEWORD

There is a nine-letter word hidden in the grid – can you find it? The nine letters form a continuous line passing through each square once, without crossing itself.

ABC LOGIC

Place the letters A, B and C exactly once in each row and column. Each row and column has two blank cells. The letters at the edge of a row/column indicate which of the letters is the first/last to appear in that row/column.

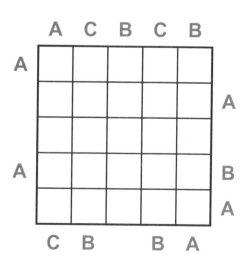

SIMPLE LOOP

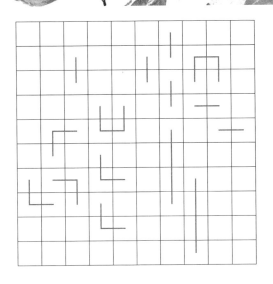

Draw a single, continuous loop that visits every square in the puzzle grid just once. The loop cannot cross itself and must enter and exit each square, so look for instances where there are only two neighbouring squares that can be visited by an empty square.

CALCUDOKU

Place the numbers from 1–6 once in each row and column, while obeying the sums in the bold-lined regions. The number specifies the total for that region while the operator shows which sum should be applied between the numbers in the region to reach the given total. Numbers may repeat within the bold-lined regions. With subtraction always take the lower numbers away from the highest number in a region, and with division divide the highest number by the lower numbers.

10+			1-		
11+	60x		160x	1-	
3÷	1-	3-		11+	
				60x	
72x			3+		

WORD PYRAMID

Fill each brick with a single letter to build a pyramid. Each row contains the same bricks as the row beneath but with one missing – however, the order may vary. Each row must spell out a word that matches its clue.

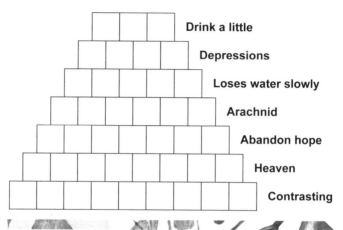

Drink a little

Depressions

Loses water slowly

Arachnid

Abandon hope

Heaven

Contrasting

KILLER SUDOKU

Place the numbers 1–6 exactly once per row, column and 3 x 2 bold-lined box. Additionally the sum total of the squares in each dashed-line shape must match the total given in that shape, and you may not repeat a number within a dashed-line shape.

7	6	7		5	
		14			10
	8		7		
8	5	10		7	
		6			9
10			7		

STACK PUZZLE

Eight pairs of flip-flops are in a pile. Can you tell which pair is at the bottom of the pile?

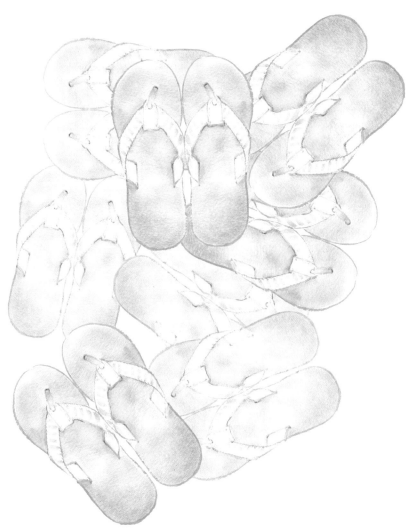

LETTERFIT

Can you place each of these words once in the grid to create a filled crossword grid?

5 letters

Bandy
Calve
Kenya
Peach
Ruddy
Shawl
Spark
Twirl

6 letters

Drover
Franks
Neared
Neaten

7 letters

Arrears
Cohabit
Foundry
Gherkin
Jacuzzi
Lapsing

8 letters

Airiness
Annotate
Catapult
Evensong

9 letters

Ancestral
Serenades

PATHFINDER

Moving from letter to adjacent letter, can you find a path that visits every square and spells out the names of several **butterflies**? Start on the shaded square.

M	M	O	N	B	L	U	E	O
O	E	R	T	E	L	G	N	R
C	D	R	A	L	E	R	I	A
W	A	I	R	B	T	E	G	N
O	D	M	I	M	I	T	I	S
L	Y	D	T	S	H	W	P	M
L	E	E	O	N	E	L	L	A
O	U	D	R	E	P	U	R	P
L	C	R	O	P	M	E	E	L

WORDWHEEL

Find as many words of three or more letters in the wheel as you can. Each word must use the central letter and a selection from the outer wheel – no letter may be used more times than it appears in the wheel. Can you find the nine-letter word hidden in the wheel?

BATTLESHIPS

Deduce the location of each ship listed below. Numbers around the edge of the grid specify the number of ship segments found in each row and column of the grid. Each ship is surrounded on all sides (horizontally, vertically and diagonally) by water.

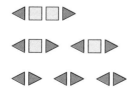

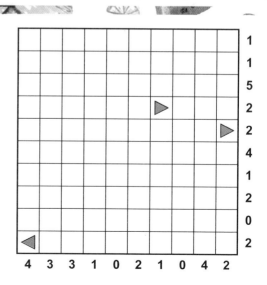

STAR LETTER

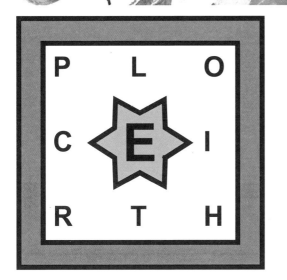

Can you find a ten-letter word that can be formed by using the star letter twice, and each other letter once?

P L O

C **E** I

R T H

JIGSAW SUDOKU

Place the numbers 1–9 once in each row, column and bold-lined jigsaw region composed of nine cells.

						1		
4	8							
6		2					5	
	4	5						
	7		4					
1	3							6
		8						
7	6							

BINARY

Fill the grid with 0s and 1s such that 0 and 1 each occur six times in each row and column. The same digit cannot occur in more than two consecutive cells either horizontally or vertically. No whole row can repeat the same series of 0s and 1s as any other row, and no whole column can repeat the same series of 0s and 1s as any other column.

1				0	0		1			1
		1	1							
1				1		0			1	
1	0						1		1	
		0		0						
					1		0		0	
			0	0		1				1
1			1			1		1		1
										0
				1			0			
0		0	0				1			
			0	1			1	1		

ABCDOKU

	D		E	A
	1	A		
		5	D	
		4		
5		B		3

Each square contains a letter and a number. Place 1–5 and A–E once in each row and column to fill the grid. Each combination from A1 through to E5 also appears exactly once in the puzzle.

WORD LADDER

Can you climb the rungs of this word ladder? Change only one letter at each step in order to move from the bottom to the top, and do not rearrange the order of the letters.

ROLL

BACK

FIND THE SUM

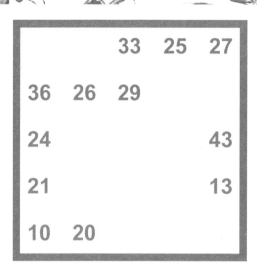

		33	25	27
36	26	29		
24				43
21				13
10	20			

Three of the numbers in this box add up to 104. But can you work out what those three numbers are?

ABC LOGIC

Place the letters A, B and C exactly once in each row and column. Each row and column has two blank cells. The letters at the edge of a row/column indicate which of the letters is the first/last to appear in that row/column.

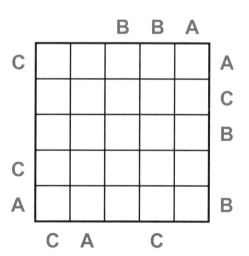

BRIDGES

Connect all the circles (which represent islands) into a single interconnected group.
The number in a circle represents the number of bridges that connect that island to
other islands. Bridges can only be created horizontally or vertically,
with no more than two bridges between any pair of islands. Bridges cannot cross any
other bridges.

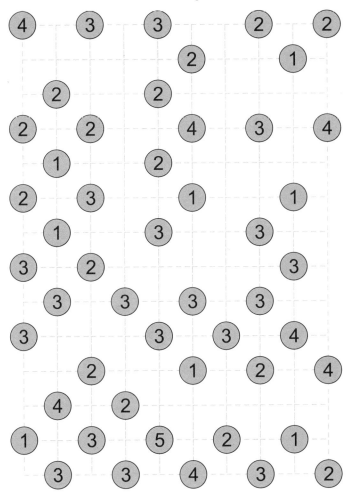

CROSSWORD

Solve the clues to complete this classic crossword puzzle.

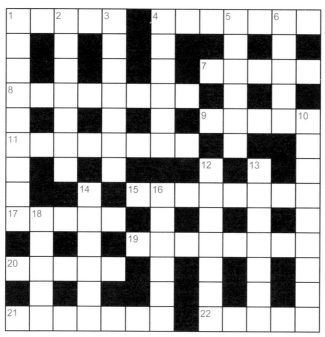

Across
1 Assertion (5)
4 Not straight (7)
7 Simple earrings (5)
8 Tied up (8)
9 Large crow (5)
11 Essential nutrients (8)
15 Clamber (8)
17 Mountain cry (5)
19 European primulas (8)
20 Lumberjack (5)
21 Herb (7)
22 Reverence for God (5)

Down
1 Imprisonment (9)
2 Disturb (7)
3 Repositories of antiques (7)
4 Meet or find by chance (4,2)
5 Expenditure (6)
6 ___ Izzard: stand-up
   comedian (5)
10 Essential (9)
12 Root vegetable (7)
13 Remove a difficulty (7)
14 Cuts off (6)
16 Hoarse (of a voice) (6)
18 Last Greek letter (5)

BATTLESHIPS

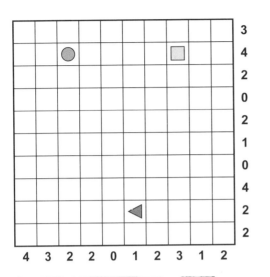

3
4
2
0
2
1
0
4
2
2

4 3 2 2 0 1 2 3 1 2

Deduce the location of each ship listed below. Numbers around the edge of the grid specify the number of ship segments found in each row and column of the grid. Each ship is surrounded on all sides (horizontally, vertically and diagonally) by water.

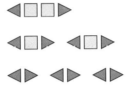

SNAKEWORD

There is a nine-letter word hidden in the grid – can you find it? The nine letters form a continuous line passing through each square once, without crossing itself.

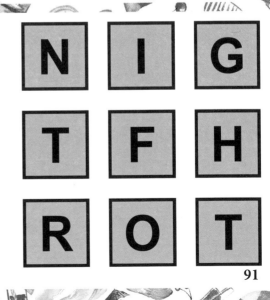

N	I	G
T	F	H
R	O	T

LETTERFIT

Can you place each of these words once in the grid to create a filled crossword grid?

3 letters

Duo
Lad

4 letters

Smug
Sore

5 letters

Divot
Egret
Femur
Flail
Gapes
Items

6 letters

Adorer
Lessee
Triads
Vanish

7 letters

Admiral
Avenged
Drapers
Excited
Ordered
Outfits
Outsize
Tendril

8 letters

Egoistic
Kinetics
Selector
Stressed

JEWELS AND GEMS

Can you find the words in this classic wordsearch grid?

```
S D T D Z M T S S C S L C S I
U L C Z P E N N P A R A A G T
T O P A Z L W H I P P P A P G
S G E G D I A F E N P R P A O
Q U A R T Z X T R H N A A F D
P E R I D O T U I E O U L P Q
M O L U S S U R T N R T N T D
Q T S T D X E R Y I U E T R K
N T A R N Q R X M R J M P S R
I O Y N O D E C L A H C T S O
Y O C L M T Y P L M L R N I E
L A B R A A B E P A Q I S L S
C B E S I O U Q R U T H N V X
P D O A D Z R A O Q L Y R E B
B O T S Y H T E M A J B L R R
```

AMETHYST	PERIDOT
AQUAMARINE	PLATINUM
BERYL	QUARTZ
CHALCEDONY	RUBY
DIAMONDS	SAPPHIRE
GARNET	SILVER
GOLD	TOPAZ
ONYX	TOURMALINE
OPAL	TURQUOISE
PEARLS	ZIRCON

93

SYMBOL VALUES

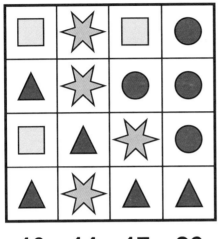

Each of the four shapes represents a positive whole number. The sum of the shapes in each row and column is displayed at the end of each row and column. Using this information can you work out the numerical value of each shape?

STAR LETTER

Can you find a ten-letter word that can be formed by using the star letter twice, and each other letter once?

FIND THE KEY

Can you find the matching key?

1

2

3

4

5

6

7

PATHFINDER

Moving from letter to adjacent letter, can you find a path that visits every square and spells out several words relating to **cheese**? Start on the shaded square.

E	R	B	Y	S	T	R	A	C
D	A	L	I	R	I	P	A	S
E	B	L	C	N	L	O	M	E
I	R	E	O	O	T	N	A	L
Z	A	R	T	T	C	E	D	Y
Z	R	O	G	A	A	E	R	E
O	G	O	N	Y	L	L	P	L
M	A	F	Z	O	L	I	H	S
O	L	F	U	B	A	W	E	N

FIND THE SUM

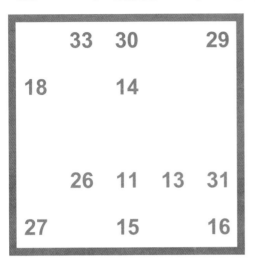

Three of the numbers in this box add up to 91. But can you work out what those three numbers are?

33 30   29

18   14

26 11 13 31

27   15   16

WORD LADDER

Can you climb the rungs of this word ladder? Change only one letter at each step in order to move from the bottom to the top, and do not rearrange the order of the letters.

READ

BOOK

KAKURO

Fill the white squares so that the total in each across or down run of cells matches the total at the start of that run. You must use the numbers from 1–9 only and cannot repeat a number in a run.

SIMPLE LOOP

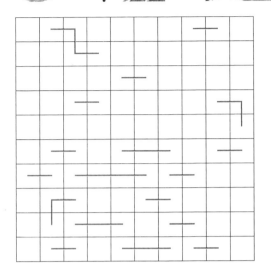

Draw a single, continuous loop that visits every square in the puzzle grid just once. The loop cannot cross itself and must enter and exit each square, so look for instances where there are only two neighbouring squares that can be visited by an empty square.

ABC LOGIC

Place the letters A, B and C exactly once in each row and column. Each row and column has two blank cells. The letters at the edge of a row/column indicate which of the letters is the first/last to appear in that row/column.

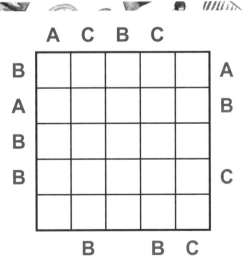

CROSSWORD

Solve the clues to complete this classic crossword puzzle.

Across

1 Suave; stylish (8)
5 Bend over on itself (4)
8 Precise (5)
9 Jumbled (5-2)
10 Not as quiet (7)
12 Area of land (7)
14 Mythical female sea creature (7)
16 Make a study of (7)
18 Japanese dish of raw fish (7)
19 Model; perfect (5)
20 Grain store (4)
21 Country of East Asia (8)

Down

1 Ruminant mammal (4)
2 Large amphibious rodent (6)
3 As might be expected (9)
4 Resistant to something (6)
6 Confer holy orders on (6)
7 Gone (8)
11 Trespassing (9)
12 US state (8)
13 Adornment of hanging threads (6)
14 Sheep known for its wool (6)
15 Be attractive (6)
17 Wingless jumping insect (4)

ABCDoku

E	A		C	
A2		4		
3		D		
		2		5
		1		

Each square contains a letter and a number. Place 1–5 and A–E once in each row and column to fill the grid. Each combination from A1 through to E5 also appears exactly once in the puzzle.

SYMBOL VALUES

Each of the four shapes represents a positive whole number. The sum of the shapes in each row and column is displayed at the end of each row and column. Using this information can you work out the numerical value of each shape?

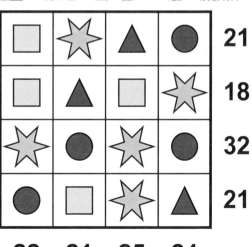

BATTLESHIPS

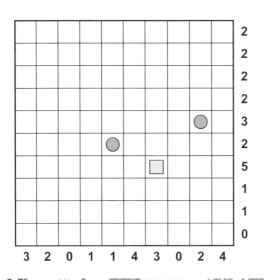

Deduce the location of each ship listed below. Numbers around the edge of the grid specify the number of ship segments found in each row and column of the grid. Each ship is surrounded on all sides (horizontally, vertically and diagonally) by water.

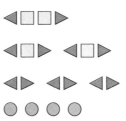

JIGSAW SUDOKU

Place the numbers 1–9 once in each row, column and bold-lined jigsaw region composed of nine cells.

CALCUDOKU

20x		8+	1-	2-	
4+				6+	
3÷	3+		11+	14+	60x
	2÷				
10+		8+	7+		

Place the numbers from 1–6 once in each row and column, while obeying the sums in the bold-lined regions. The number specifies the total for that region while the operator shows which sum should be applied between the numbers in the region to reach the given total. Numbers may repeat within the bold-lined regions. With subtraction always take the lower numbers away from the highest number in a region, and with division divide the highest number by the lower numbers.

SNAKEWORD

There is a nine-letter word hidden in the grid – can you find it? The nine letters form a continuous line passing through each square once, without crossing itself.

WORD LADDER

TAKE

HEED

Can you climb the rungs of this word ladder? Change only one letter at each step in order to move from the bottom to the top, and do not rearrange the order of the letters.

WORD PYRAMID

Fill each brick with a single letter to build a pyramid. Each row contains the same bricks as the row beneath but with one missing – however, the order may vary. Each row must spell out a word that matches its clue.

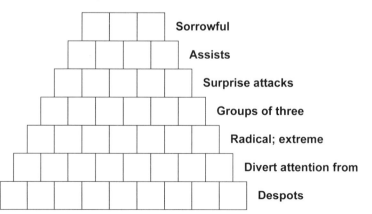

Sorrowful

Assists

Surprise attacks

Groups of three

Radical; extreme

Divert attention from

Despots

WORDWHEEL

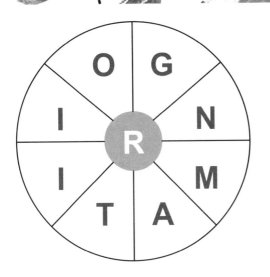

Find as many words of three or more letters in the wheel as you can. Each word must use the central letter and a selection from the outer wheel – no letter may be used more times than it appears in the wheel. Can you find the nine-letter word hidden in the wheel?

KILLER SUDOKU

Place the numbers 1–6 exactly once per row, column and 3 x 2 bold-lined box. Additionally the sum total of the squares in each dashed-line shape must match the total given in that shape, and you may not repeat a number within a dashed-line shape.

13		8			7
9		9	8		
	3			8	
13		9	7	10	
				10	
4		8			

STAR LETTER

Can you find a ten-letter word that can be formed by using the star letter twice, and each other letter once?

ABC LOGIC

Place the letters A, B and C exactly once in each row and column. Each row and column has two blank cells. The letters at the edge of a row/column indicate which of the letters is the first/last to appear in that row/column.

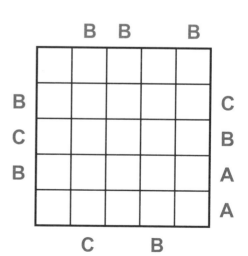

LETTERFIT

Can you place each of these words once in the grid to create a filled crossword grid?

3 letters

Arc
Pro

4 letters

Aped
Care
Look
Owes

5 letters

Asset
Excel
Heirs
Oiled
React
Scans

6 letters

Poetry
Traces

7 letters

Archaic
College
Conceal
Deplete
Forceps
Neatest
Occlude
Spurred

8 letters

Concrete
Precious

9 letters

Certitude
Isometric

SOLUTIONS

Page 3

Page 5

		E	T	A				
	T	E	A	L				
	L	A	T	E	R			
R	E	T	A	I	L			
R	E	A	L	I	T	Y		
L	I	T	E	R	A	C	Y	
C	E	R	T	A	I	N	L	Y

Circle: 6, Square: 4, Triangle: 8, Star: 7

Page 4

C3	B2	D5	A4	E1
A5	E3	B1	D2	C4
E2	D4	A3	C1	B5
B4	A1	C2	E5	D3
D1	C5	E4	B3	A2

DOOR
DOER
DEER
SEER
SEEP
STEP

Page 6

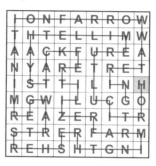

Page 7

Wordwheel: Condition

2	4	6	1	3	5
5	3	1	6	2	4
1	5	4	2	6	3
6	2	3	5	4	1
3	1	2	4	5	6
4	6	5	3	1	2

SOLUTIONS

Page 8

Page 9

Snakeword: Afterlife

Page 10

C	R	U	N	C	H		B		F	O	P
	A		O		S	O	L	V	E		E
R	I	N	G	L	E	T		O	R		T
	D		O		A		C	O	R	G	I
D	E	A	F	N	E	S	S		A		O
	R		I		H		D		R		L
I	S	S	U	E	D		R	E	C	I	P	E
N		T		S		E		R		A	
S		A		O	M	N	I	V	O	R	E
U	N	D	I	D		E		S		V	
R		I		A		R	O	O	M	I	E	R
E	U	N	I	T	Y		R		E	N	
D	I	M		S		G	Y	P	S	U	M

Page 11

Star Letter: Contribute

5	3	4	6	1	2
6	5	1	2	4	3
3	1	6	4	2	5
2	6	5	1	3	4
4	2	3	5	6	1
1	4	2	3	5	6

Page 12

				16	9	22			
		5	3	6	3	1	2	13	11
3	2	1	7	7	8	9	18 17	8	9
11	3	2	1	5	11	3	1	5	2
	12	14	3	2	1	17	8	9	11	16
9	3	2	4			11	8	1	2
17	8	9	6			10 16	7	9
6	1	3	2	13		21 9	1	3	5
11	4	3	1	16	9	7	8	13
10	4	3	1	2	11 11	3	2	1	5
8	7	1	24	7	9	8	15	7	8
			6	3	2	1			

SOLUTIONS

Page 13

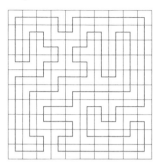

1	2	6	8	3	9	7	5	4
3	4	2	6	5	8	9	1	7
7	5	4	3	1	2	8	9	6
9	7	1	4	6	5	2	8	3
5	6	9	2	4	7	1	3	8
6	9	3	7	8	4	5	2	1
4	8	7	9	2	1	3	6	5
8	3	5	1	9	6	4	7	2
2	1	8	5	7	3	6	4	9

Page 14

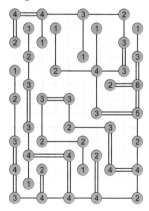

Page 15

Find the Sum: 29, 34, 39

Page 16

Page 17

Find the Key: 6

Page 18

0	1	0	0	1	0	1	0	1	0	1	1
1	1	0	1	1	0	0	1	0	0	1	0
1	0	1	1	0	1	1	0	0	1	0	0
0	0	1	0	0	1	1	0	1	1	0	1
1	1	0	0	1	0	0	1	0	0	1	1
1	0	1	1	0	1	0	1	0	0	1	0
0	0	1	0	1	0	1	0	1	1	0	1
0	1	0	0	1	1	0	0	1	1	0	1
1	0	1	1	0	0	1	1	0	0	1	0
0	1	0	1	0	0	1	1	0	1	0	1
0	1	1	0	1	1	0	0	1	1	0	0
1	0	0	1	0	1	0	1	1	0	1	0

SOLUTIONS

Page 19

GOOD
GOLD
BOLD
BALD
BALL
CALL

Page 20

Page 21

A	P	P	O	S	I	T	E		I	T	E	M
W		E		U	H			E		E		O
R	U	L	E	S		R	E	S	I	D	E	D
Y		L		P	I			I		E		
		E		E		L	A	C	Q	U	E	R
O	P	T	I	C	A	L		O	M	A		A
V				T				U		T		
E		T	E		A	I	R	L	I	N	E	
R	O	U	N	D	E	D		T		N		
R		S			O		R	N		U		
I	N	S	U	L	A	R		O	V	A	L	S
D		L			E		O		T		E	
E	K	E	S		B	R	I	M	L	E	S	S

Page 22

Wordwheel: Continent

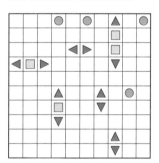

Page 23

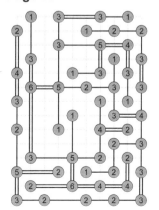

111

SOLUTIONS

Page 24

Snakeword: Evaporate

Star Letter: Relaxation

Page 25

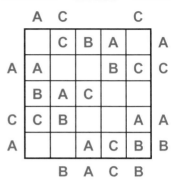

Page 26

Page 27

Circle: 6, Square: 5, Triangle: 4, Star: 3

Page 28

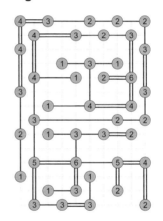

Page 29

	1	2	3	4
A	6	1	8	
B	2			
C	3	7	5 4	

SOLUTIONS

A2	B5	E1	C3	D4
E3	A1	C4	D5	B2
C5	E4	D2	B1	A3
D1	C2	B3	A4	E5
B4	D3	A5	E2	C1

Snakeword: Calibrate

5	9	1	7	3	4	2	8	6
4	2	6	3	8	7	1	5	9
1	8	7	6	5	9	4	2	3
8	4	2	1	7	6	9	3	5
7	6	8	2	9	5	3	1	4
3	5	9	4	1	2	6	7	8
6	3	5	9	2	1	8	4	7
2	7	4	8	6	3	5	9	1
9	1	3	5	4	8	7	6	2

A	P	P	R	L	E	R	C	R
H	L	Y	U	A	G	P	S	I
R	E	H	O	C	S	S	B	E
R	A	T	A	R	R	B	T	V
S	B	C	S	N	E	E	H	E
R	A	H	G	E	L	O	G	R
U	L	I	N	W	D	R	U	A
G	R	E	P	S	N	D	A	G
E	R	P	A	L	A	D	R	E

6	1	5	2	3	4
2	4	3	6	1	5
3	2	4	5	6	1
4	3	2	1	5	6
5	6	1	3	4	2
1	5	6	4	2	3

SOLUTIONS

Page 34

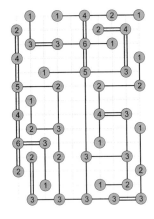

Page 35

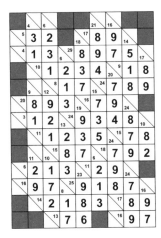

Page 36

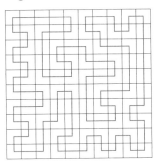

Find the Sum: 37, 38, 43

Page 37

P	O	L	I	C	E	W	O	M	A	N		
T		P		M		S		N		R		I
R		I		P	E	C	K	S		G	E	L
A	N	N	U	L		U		E		U		L
N		I	O		D		T	H	E	R	M	
S	N	O	W	D	R	O	P				A	
P		N		E			B		S		N	
O			A	B	E	R	D	E	E	N		
R	I	O	J	A		I	E		C		E	
T		P		M		K		A	L	T	A	R
E	Y	E		I	L	I	A	D		I		E
D		N		G		N		T		O		D
	A	S	T	O	N	I	S	H	I	N	G	

Page 38

R	A	C	E		A	S	S	E	S	S	O	R
E		A		B		N		N		Y		E
C	O	M	M	U	T	E		C	O	M	I	C
I		E		T		E		R		P		E
P	I	L	O	T		R	O	O	F	T	O	P
R				E		S		A		O		T
O	N	W	A	R	D		S	C	A	M	P	I
C		E		S		S		H				V
A	N	A	R	C	H	Y		M	I	N	C	E
T		K		O		M		E		E		N
I	N	E	P	T		B	A	N	D	A	G	E
O		S		C		O		T		R		S
N	U	T	S	H	E	L	L		A	S	K	S

SOLUTIONS

Page 39

1	3	4	2	6	5
5	2	6	1	4	3
3	6	1	4	5	2
4	5	2	3	1	6
2	4	5	6	3	1
6	1	3	5	2	4

Phrase: Fish out of water

Page 40

S	S	D	U	T	R	K	A	L	S	T	O	B	X	A
K	O	U	M	M	P	Q	R	W	P	R	W	E	D	V
R	S	T	U	N	J	L	U	Q	U	A	N	P	E	E
E	N	I	M	O	R	B	I	F	T	O	R	X	I	A
V	H	L	Q	T	G	O	L	D	N	W	U	G	T	R
L	R	Y	K	P	B	U	T	C	O	C	O	T	O	H
I	O	P	D	Y	O	G	H	A	C	A	R	B	O	N
S	X	A	U	R	R	L	M	L	I	T	H	I	U	M
G	Y	B	I	K	O	L	S	U	L	M	S	S	S	B
I	G	N	R	R	N	G	Q	M	I	U	N	A	T	R
A	E	Y	I	U	B	U	E	S	L	S	U	F	W	
L	N	N	P	L	A	T	I	N	U	M	E	E	L	C
N	E	N	E	G	O	R	T	I	N	W	K	H	P	S
P	B	E	R	Y	L	L	I	U	M	P	R	E	S	T
P	O	T	A	S	S	I	U	M	R	V	L	S	E	F

Page 41

LAST
CAST
CASE
CAME
TAME
TIME

9	8	5	7	3	4	1	2	6
8	3	1	2	7	6	5	4	9
1	4	6	5	2	9	7	3	8
5	2	7	4	9	1	6	8	3
2	7	3	6	1	8	9	5	4
6	9	4	1	5	3	8	7	2
4	6	2	9	8	5	3	1	7
7	5	8	3	6	2	4	9	1
3	1	9	8	4	7	2	6	5

Page 42

Snakeword: Malicious

	C	A	C	B	
		A	C	B	
	C		B		A
	B		A	C	
		C		A	B
A	A	B			C
		B	A	A	

SOLUTIONS

Page 43

	C	Y	B	E	R	N	E	T	I	C	S	
D		I		X		U	R		A		B
I		E		T	H	R	E	E		C	H	I
S	O	L	A	R		S		K		H		R
S		D		A		E		S	P	E	N	D
O	V	E	R	C	A	S	T					W
L		D		T			F		S			A
U				I	M	P	L	I	C	I	T	
T	H	R	U	M		A		O		O		C
I		A		O		S		W	O	R	T	H
O	D	D		U	N	T	I	E		P		E
N		A		L		I		R		I		R
	P	R	E	D	E	C	E	S	S	O	R	

Page 44

0	1	1	0	1	0	1	0	0	1	1	0
0	0	1	1	0	0	1	0	1	0	1	1
1	0	0	1	0	1	0	1	0	1	0	1
1	1	0	0	1	0	1	0	1	1	0	0
0	1	1	0	1	0	0	1	0	0	1	1
0	0	1	1	0	1	1	0	1	0	0	1
1	1	0	0	1	0	1	1	0	1	0	0
1	1	0	1	0	1	0	0	1	0	1	0
0	0	1	1	0	1	0	1	0	0	1	1
0	1	0	0	1	0	1	0	1	1	0	1
1	0	1	0	1	1	0	1	0	1	0	0
1	0	0	1	0	1	0	1	1	0	1	0

Page 45

C2	E4	D3	B1	A5
E1	B3	A2	D5	C4
B5	D2	C1	A4	E3
A3	C5	B4	E2	D1
D4	A1	E5	C3	B2

Star Letter: Dishearten

Page 46

6	2	3	4	5	1
3	5	6	1	4	2
1	4	5	3	2	6
4	3	1	2	6	5
5	1	2	6	3	4
2	6	4	5	1	3

	B		C	C	
B	C			A	A
	A	C		B	B
B	B	A	C		
C	C		B	A	A
A	A			B	C
	B		B		

Page 47

SOLUTIONS

Page 48

1	1	0	1	0	1	1	0	0	1	0	0
1	0	1	1	0	1	0	1	0	1	0	0
0	0	1	0	1	0	0	1	1	0	1	1
1	1	0	0	1	0	1	0	0	1	0	1
0	1	0	1	0	1	0	1	1	0	1	0
1	0	1	0	1	1	0	0	1	0	1	0
0	1	0	0	1	0	1	1	0	1	0	1
1	0	1	1	0	0	1	0	1	0	0	1
0	1	0	0	1	1	0	1	1	0	1	0
0	1	0	0	1	0	1	1	0	1	1	0
1	0	1	1	0	0	1	0	0	1	0	1
0	0	1	1	0	1	0	0	1	0	1	1

Page 49

		S	U	N			
	S	T	U	N			
	T	U	R	N	S		
S	A	T	U	R	N		
S	A	U	N	T	E	R	
N	E	U	T	R	A	L	S
R	E	S	U	L	T	A	N	T

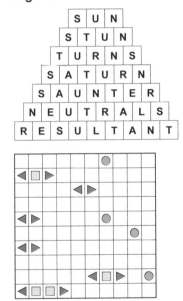

Page 50

Circle: 4, Square: 2, Triangle: 6, Star: 3

2	6	1	5	3	4
5	3	6	1	4	2
6	2	5	4	1	3
4	1	3	2	5	6
3	5	4	6	2	1
1	4	2	3	6	5

Page 51

SOLUTIONS

Page 52

2	5	6	4	3	1
3	1	4	6	2	5
6	2	3	1	5	4
1	4	5	3	6	2
4	6	2	5	1	3
5	3	1	2	4	6

Snakeword: Champagne

Page 53

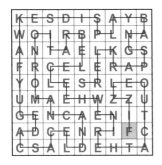

Page 54

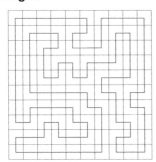

Phrase: Cliffhanger

Page 55

Page 56

Page 57

MAIN
MAID
LAID
LAND
LANE
LINE

SOLUTIONS

Circle: 1, Square: 10, Triangle: 2, Star: 7

Page 58

S	T	C			P	S		D	
C	O	U	G	H	S		E	R	M	I	N	E
E		T		A		P		O		F		T
P	R	O	V	I	S	O		L	I	T	R	E
T		R		R		L		O		S		R
R	E	E	D		E	L	A	N	D			
E		D		T		U		G		U		H
			F	I	F	T	H		O	S	L	O
E		A		T		A		O		E		U
L	E	M	M	A		N	O	Z	Z	L	E	S
E		B		N		T		O		E		I
C	O	L	L	I	E		U	N	I	S	O	N
T		E		C			S		S		G	

Page 59

Find the Sum: 17, 20, 28

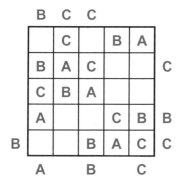

	B	C	C	
		C		B	A	
	B	A	C			C
	C	B	A		
	A			C	B	B
B			B	A	C	C
	A		B		C	

Page 60

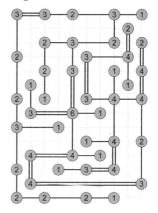

Page 61

B	E	E	R	F	O	U	A	I
O	S	A	C	R	E	R	M	D
U	E	E	P	P	P	R	E	E
N	W	S	E	I	O	B	G	N
D	R	O	S	L	W	I	N	F
A	L	U	R	F	R	E	I	I
R	L	N	E	V	E	R	W	E
Y	A	D	E	R	I	N	S	L
E	R	I	P	M	U	R	E	D

Page 62

Star Letter: Figurehead

8	9	2	7	3	1	6	5	4
5	1	6	8	4	2	3	7	9
4	8	1	9	7	5	2	3	6
3	6	4	2	5	7	1	9	8
7	3	9	4	6	8	5	2	1
6	5	8	3	2	9	4	1	7
9	2	3	1	8	4	7	6	5
1	7	5	6	9	3	8	4	2
2	4	7	5	1	6	9	8	3

SOLUTIONS

Page 63

```
R B L Z M V V P K B A N N E Y
G P A W N O I N O M E L O N U
W O Y N V B O S T A M S E P E
R M R B A W Y R R E H C U R Z
S E T U R N I P H W M V I P G
U G C L W O A S O S S A U I R
Y R R E B W A R T S U T A F L
Y A A L S T D F B G M U G F
G N S A P E G A B B A C A E F
V A P U V E R F E E R A T D T
L T B A Z O F Y I M A I Y O Z
I E E A I A C R F G P N Q B T
T M R E L P P A U G S Q P O T
X H N O S M A D I A H E J I
I A Y I A P R I C O T G G S F
```

Page 64

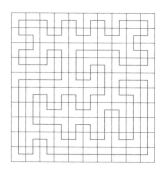

```
6 2 5 4 1 3
4 1 3 6 2 5
1 3 6 5 4 2
5 4 2 3 6 1
3 6 1 2 5 4
2 5 4 1 3 6
```

Page 65

```
4 2 1 6 5 3
5 1 6 4 3 2
2 4 3 1 6 5
1 5 4 3 2 6
6 3 5 2 4 1
3 6 2 5 1 4
```

Page 66

Circle: 4, Square: 5, Triangle: 2, Star: 9

```
      C   C   B
    C       B       A
A           A   B   C   C
A   A   C           B   B
    B   A       C       C
B       B   C   A       A
      B   B   C   A
```

SOLUTIONS

Page 67

Page 68

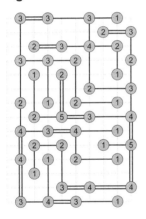

Page 69

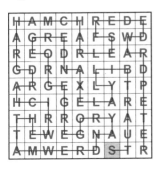

Page 70

Wordwheel: Developed

Star Letter: Ungrateful

Page 71

Page 72

0	0	1	0	0	1	0	1	1	0	1	1
1	0	0	1	0	0	1	0	1	1	0	1
0	1	0	0	1	1	0	1	0	1	1	0
1	0	1	0	1	1	0	0	1	0	0	1
0	0	1	1	0	0	1	0	1	1	0	1
0	1	0	1	0	1	1	0	0	1	0	0
1	1	0	0	1	1	0	0	1	0	1	0
0	0	1	1	0	1	1	0	0	1	0	1
1	1	0	1	1	0	0	1	0	0	1	0
0	1	0	1	0	0	1	1	0	1	0	0
1	0	1	0	0	1	1	0	0	1	0	1
1	1	0	1	0	0	1	1	0	1	0	0

Page 73

121

SOLUTIONS

Page 74

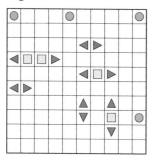

Snakeword: Condemned

Page 75

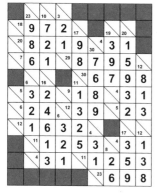

Page 76

4	6	5	7	8	3	9	1	2
8	1	4	6	2	7	3	5	9
3	8	9	1	5	2	4	7	6
2	9	1	5	4	6	7	3	8
5	3	6	9	7	1	2	8	4
9	7	3	4	1	8	6	2	5
1	2	8	3	6	4	5	9	7
7	4	2	8	9	5	1	6	3
6	5	7	2	3	9	8	4	1

Snakeword: Impassive

Page 77

Page 78

Snakeword: Eliminate

	A	C	B	C	B	
A	A			C	B	
		C	B	A		A
	B		A		C	
A		A	C	B		B
	C	B			A	A
	C	B		B	A	

SOLUTIONS

Page 79

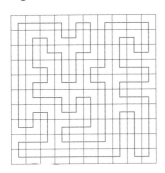

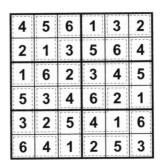

4	5	6	1	3	2
2	1	3	5	6	4
1	6	2	3	4	5
5	3	4	6	2	1
3	2	5	4	1	6
6	4	1	2	5	3

Page 81

5	1	4	3	6	2
6	2	5	4	1	3
2	3	6	5	4	1
3	4	1	2	5	6
1	5	2	6	3	4
4	6	3	1	2	5

Page 80

```
        S I P
      D I P S
    D R I P S
  S P I D E R
D E S P A I R
P A R A D I S E
D I S P A R A T E
```

Page 82

```
S H A W L     F O U N D R Y
E   R   A     R     E     U
R   R   P     A   B A N D Y
E V E N S O N G     R     D
N   A   I   K   K E N Y A
A I R I N E S S     D       N
D   S   G       C   J     C
E     D   A N N O T A T E
S P A R K     E   H   C   S
    E   O   C A T A P U L T
C A L V E     T   B   Z   R
    C   E     E   I   Z   A
G H E R K I N     T W I R L
```

SOLUTIONS

Page 83

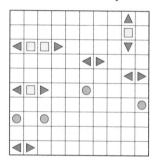

M	M	O	N	B	L	U	E	O
O	E	R	T	E	L	G	N	R
C	D	R	A	L	E	R		A
W	A	I	R	B	T	E	G	N
O	D	M	I	M	I	T	H	S
L	Y	D	T	S	H	W	P	M
L	E	E	O	N	E	L	L	A
O	U	D	R	E	P	U	R	P
L	C	R	O	P	M	E	E	L

Page 84

Wordwheel: Literally

Page 85

Star Letter: Helicopter

3	2	1	7	8	9	6	4	5
9	5	7	6	4	8	1	2	3
4	8	3	2	5	6	7	9	1
6	9	2	3	1	7	8	5	4
8	4	5	1	9	2	3	6	7
5	7	6	4	2	1	9	3	8
1	3	4	9	7	5	2	8	6
2	1	8	5	6	3	4	7	9
7	6	9	8	3	4	5	1	2

Page 86

1	0	0	1	1	0	0	1	1	0	0	1
0	0	1	1	0	1	1	0	0	1	0	1
1	1	0	0	1	0	1	0	0	1	1	0
1	0	1	0	0	1	0	1	1	0	1	0
0	1	0	1	0	1	1	0	0	1	0	1
1	1	0	1	0	1	0	0	1	0	0	0
0	0	1	0	0	1	0	1	1	0	1	1
1	0	0	1	0	0	1	0	1	0	1	1
0	1	1	0	1	0	1	0	1	0	0	0
1	1	0	1	1	0	0	1	0	0	1	0
0	1	0	0	1	0	0	1	1	0	1	1
0	1	1	0	0	1	1	0	1	0	1	0

Page 87

B4	D5	C2	E3	A1
D2	C1	A3	B5	E4
C3	A4	E5	D1	B2
E1	B3	D4	A2	C5
A5	E2	B1	C4	D3

ROLL
TOLL
TALL
TALK
TACK
BACK

124

SOLUTIONS

Page 88

Find the Sum: 25, 36, 43

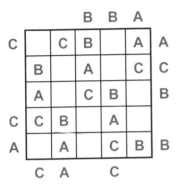

Page 89

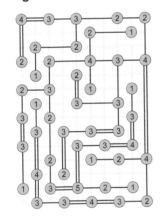

Page 90

Page 91

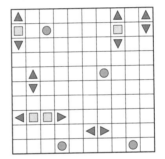

Snakeword: Fortnight

Page 92

SOLUTIONS

Page 93

Page 94

Circle: 8, Square: 3, Triangle: 2, Star: 4

Star Letter: Watermelon

Page 95

Find the Key: 4

Page 96

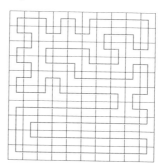

Page 97

Find the Sum: 27, 31, 33

Page 98

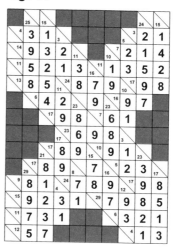

Page 99

READ
BEAD
BEAT
BOAT
BOOT
BOOK

SOLUTIONS

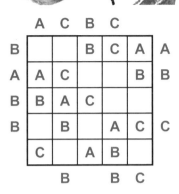

Page 102

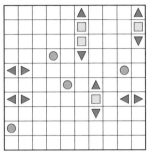

4	6	7	9	1	5	3	8	2
5	3	9	1	7	8	2	4	6
2	8	4	3	6	9	1	7	5
6	7	2	5	3	4	9	1	8
3	4	5	2	8	1	7	6	9
9	1	8	7	5	6	4	2	3
8	2	3	6	4	7	5	9	1
7	5	1	8	9	2	6	3	4
1	9	6	4	2	3	8	5	7

Page 100

D	E	B	O	N	A	I	R		F	O	L	D
E		E		A		M			R			E
E	X	A	C	T		M	I	X	E	D	U	P
R		V		U		U			A			A
		E		R		N	O	I	S	I	E	R
A	C	R	E	A	G	E		N		N		T
R		L		L		T		T				E
K		T		L		M	E	R	M	A	I	D
A	N	A	L	Y	S	E		U		P		
N		S		R		D		D		P		F
S	A	S	H	I	M	I		I	D	E	A	L
A		E		N		N		N		A		E
S	I	L	O		M	O	N	G	O	L	I	A

Page 101

E4	A5	B3	C1	D2
A2	D3	C4	E5	B1
C3	E1	D5	B2	A4
D1	B4	E2	A3	C5
B5	C2	A1	D4	E3

Circle: 6, Square: 3, Triangle: 2, Star: 10

Page 103

5	4	2	6	1	3
3	1	6	5	2	4
6	2	1	4	3	5
2	6	4	3	5	1
4	3	5	1	6	2
1	5	3	2	4	6

Snakeword: Gentleman

SOLUTIONS

Page 104

| TAKE |
| HAKE |
| HARE |
| HARD |
| HERD |
| HEED |

```
        S A D
      A I D S
    R A I D S
  T R I A D S
D R A S T I C
D I S T R A C T
D I C T A T O R S
```

Page 105

Wordwheel: Migration

3	6	2	1	5	4
5	4	1	6	2	3
4	1	3	5	6	2
6	2	5	4	3	1
2	5	4	3	1	6
1	3	6	2	4	5

Page 106

Star Letter: Introduced

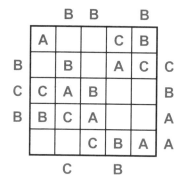

```
      B   B        B
  | A |   |   | C | B |
B |   | B |   | A | C | C
C | C | A | B |   |   | B
B | B | C | A |   |   | A
  |   |   | C | B | A | A
      C       B
```

Page 107

```
O   C   D   T   S   C   O
I S O M E T R I C   A R C
L   N   P   A   A   R   C
E X C E L   C O N C E A L
D   R   E   E   S       U
    N E A T E S T   A P E D
F   T   E       A   R   E
O W E S   S P U R R E D
R       R   O   C   C   A
C O L L E G E   H E I R S
E   O   A   T   A   O   S
P R O   C E R T I T U D E
S   K   T   Y   C   S   T
```